NOVELLO'S ORIGINAL OCTAVO EDITION.

GIVE THE HUNGRY MAN THY BREAD

(BRICH DEM HUNGRIGEN DEIN BROD)

A CANTATA

FOR SOLI, CHORUS AND ORCHESTRA

COMPOSED BY

J. S. BACH.

EDITED BY JOHN E. WEST.
ENGLISH VERSION BY PAUL ENGLAND.

PRICE ONE SHILLING.

LONDON: NOVELLO AND COMPANY, LIMITED.
NEW YORK: THE H. W. GRAY CO., SOLE AGENTS FOR THE U.S.A.

CONTENTS.

———·———

PART I.

PART II.

GIVE THE HUNGRY MAN THY BREAD.

PART I.

CHORUS.
Andante moderato. ♩ = 72.

Johann Sebastian Bach.

12509

4

12509

de - so - - late bring them in - to thy house.

men in - to thy house, bring them to thy house.

- late bring to thy house, Give the hun - gry man thy bread, and them that are

de - so - late bring_____ to thy house.

Give the hun - gry man thy

de - - so - late bring to thy house, and them that are de - so-

B

6

8

-late, are de - so - late, bring _____ to thy house. Give the hungry man thy

de - so - late, bring _____ to thy house. Give the hungry man thy

that are de-so-late bring _____ to thy house. Give the hungry man thy

_____ are de - so-late bring _____ to thy house. Give the hungry man thy

bread, give the hungry man thy

bread, give the hungry man thy

bread, give the hungry man thy

bread, give the hungry man thy

10

them that are de — — so — late bring_____ to thy

that are de — — so — late, are de — so — late, bring them in — to thy

de — so — late man in — to thy house, bring him in — to thy

de — so — late, are de — so — — late, bring_____ to thy

Andante Allegro.

house. So co — — ver him, so co — — —

house. So co — — ver him, if any thou seeest

house. So co — — ver him,

house. If any thou seeest na — ked, so co — ver him,

Andante Allegro. ♩ = 72.

12

C

18

12509

- ry of the Lord shall a - rise up - on

Alto.

And the glo - - ry of the Lord shall a - rise up -

-on thee, a -

thee, and the

22

RECITATIVE.
Bass.

With la-vish hand our God on us His boun-ty showers, To

Him a - lone our ve - ry breath we owe; All that we

have is His; a plen-teous feast is ours, But not___ that

we a-lone a sel-fish joy might know; He bids us bear in

mind that as, by His good will To us, who no-thing own, have

all good things been granted, So we should ne - ver fail of our a -

- bun - dant store To give where help is want-ed. He wills not that the

slaughter'd vic - tim bleed, Burnt off'rings please Him not with plea-sant

sa - vour; Be mer - ci - ful and give to all who need, So

shall thy humble gift with God the Lord find fa - - - vour.

cresc.

p Lento.

AIR.

Andantino. ♪ = 126.

God's en--sam-ple___ thus__ to fol-low,___ Though in

hol - low, 'Tis to taste— of Heav'n be - low.

mf

By our— alms this truth— con - fess- - ing, Sow—

p

dim.

we__ here the seeds of bless__ing That here-aft - - - - -er we shall__ know,_____ That here-aft-er we shall know.

E

this truth con - fess - ing, Sow we here the

seeds of bless - ing That here - aft - er we shall know.

PART II.

*AIR.

* The Editor is responsible for the upper and inner parts of the accompaniment to this Air, Bach having supplied merely a Bass.

-la - tions our God is well pleased.

Do thine alms and have com-pas-sion, do thine alms and have com-

-pas-sion; for-get thou not, for-get thou not, for - get thou

37

12509

38

From ___ my low - ly sta - tion, Make ___ my

poor ___ ob - la ___ tion, Thou my ser - vice ___ wilt not slight.

Yet when I be - fore Thy sight,

From ___ my low - ly sta - tion, Make ___ my

poor ob - - la - - tion, Thou my ser - vice wilt_____ not slight, Thou my

ser - vice wilt not __ slight, Thou my ser - vice wilt __ not slight,

(rall.)

Thou my ser - vice wilt_____ not __ slight.

(a tempo)

RECITATIVE.

Ah, Lord, how can I hope a fit re-turn to ren-der For all the bound-less love that Thou to me hast shown? Yea, still to me dost show— for, ev'- ry pass-ing hour, Each bless-ing I re-ceive I know is Thine a-lone. My soul is all I have— and that to Thee is

giv - en— My ac - tive powers are pledged to lend my neigh-bour

aid— The need - y well may claim the goods that Thou hast

lent me— And this poor earth - ly frame must soon in earth be

laid. I bring Thee what I can; Lord! hear my hum - ble

prayer, That of Thy pro-mised bliss I too may have my share. *Lento.*

cresc.

p

CHORALE.("Freu' dich sehr O meine Seele.")

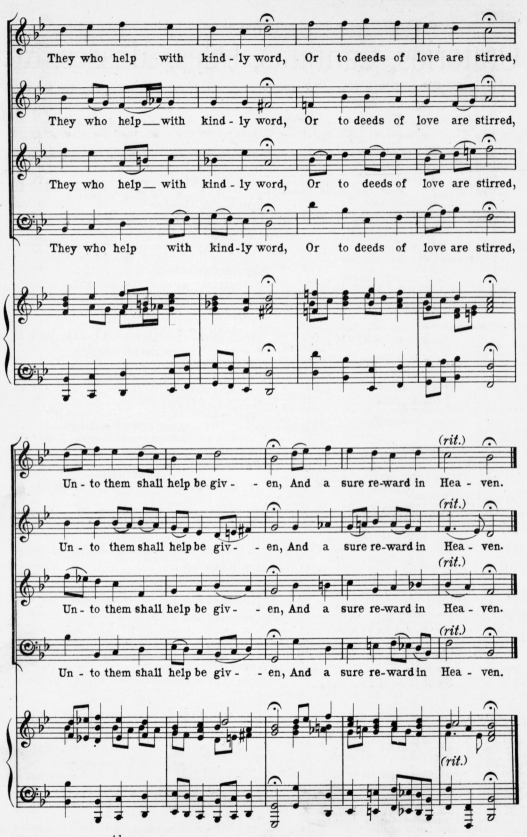

They who help with kind-ly word, Or to deeds of love are stirred,

Un - to them shall help be giv - - en, And a sure re-ward in Hea - ven.

NOVELLO'S ORIGINAL OCTAVO EDITIONS

OF

Oratorios, Cantatas, Odes, Masses, &c.

	Paper Cover.	Paper Boards.	Cloth Gilt.
FRANZ ABT.			
FAYS' FROLIC (Female voices) (Sol-fa, 0/6)	1/6	—	—
GOLDEN CITY (ditto) (Sol-fa, 0/6)	1/6	—	—
MINSTER BELLS (ditto) (Sol-fa, 0/6)	1/6	—	—
SILVER CLOUD (ditto) (Sol-fa, 0/6)	1/6	—	—
SPRINGTIME (ditto) (Sol-fa, 0/6)	1/6	—	—
SUMMER (ditto) (Sol-fa, 0/6)	1/6	—	—
WATER FAIRIES (ditto) (Sol-fa, 0/6)	1/6	—	—
WISHING STONE (ditto) (Sol-fa, 0/6)	1/6	—	—
J. H. ADAMS.			
A DAY IN SUMMER (Female Voices) (Sol-fa, 0/6)	1/6	—	—
KING CONOR ... (Sol-fa, 1/0)	2/0	2/6	4/0
THOMAS ADAMS.			
CROSS OF CHRIST (Scl-fa, 0/6)	1/0	—	—
GOLDEN HARVEST (Sol-fa, 0/8)	1/0	—	—
HOLY CHILD (Sol-fa, 0/6)	1/0	—	—
RAINBOW OF PEACE (Harvest)	1/0	—	—
B. AGUTTER.			
MISSA DE BEATA MARIÂ VIRGINE, IN C (English) (Female voices)	2/6	—	—
MISSA DE SANCTO ALBANO (English)	3/0	4/0	5/0
A. H. ALLEN.			
NEWFOUNDLAND (Ode)	1/0	—	—
THOMAS ANDERTON.			
THE NORMAN BARON	1/0	1/6	—
WRECK OF THE HESPERUS (Sol-fa, 0/4)	1/0	—	—
YULE TIDE	1/6	2/0	3/0
J. H. ANGER.			
A SONG OF THANKSGIVING	1/0	—	—
W. I. ARGENT.			
MASS, IN B FLAT (St. Benedict)	2/6	—	—
P. ARMES.			
HEZEKIAH	2/6	—	—
ST. BARNABAS	2/0	—	—
ST. JOHN THE EVANGELIST	2/6	—	—
A. D. ARNOTT.			
THE BALLAD OF CARMILHAN (Sol-fa, 1/6)	2/6	—	—
YOUNG LOCHINVAR (Sol-fa, 0/6)	1/6	—	—
E. ASPA.			
ENDYMION (with Recitation)	2/6	—	—
THE GIPSIES	1/0	—	—
ASTORGA.			
STABAT MATER	1/0	1/6	—
IVOR ATKINS.			
HYMN OF FAITH	1/6	—	—
J. C. BACH.			
I WRESTLE AND PRAY (Motet) (Sol-fa, 0/2)	0/4	—	—
J. S. BACH.			
A STRONGHOLD SURE (Sol-fa, Choruses only, 0/6)	1/0	—	—
BE NOT AFRAID (Motet) (Sol-fa, 0/4)	0/6	—	—
DITTO (New Edition)	0/8	—	—
BIDE WITH US (Sol-fa, 0/6)	1/0	—	—
BLESSING, GLORY, AND WISDOM	0/6	—	—
CHRIST LAY IN DEATH'S DARK PRISON	1/0	—	—
CHRISTMAS ORATORIO	2/0	2/6	4/0
DITTO (PARTS 1 & 2) (Sol-fa, 0/6)	1/0	—	—
DITTO (PARTS 3 & 4)	1/0	—	—
DITTO (PARTS 5 & 6)	1/0	—	—
COME, JESU, COME (Motet)	1/0	—	—
COME, REDEEMER OF OUR RACE	1/0	—	—
FROM DEPTHS OF WOE I CALL ON THEE	1/0	—	—
GIVE THE HUNGRY MAN THY BREAD	1/0	—	—
GOD GOETH UP WITH SHOUTING	1/0	—	—
GOD SO LOVED THE WORLD	1/0	—	—
GOD'S TIME IS THE BEST (Sol-fa, 0/6)	1/0	—	—
HOW BRIGHTLY SHINES	1/0	—	—
IF THOU BUT SUFFEREST GOD TO GUIDE	1/0	—	—
JESU, PRICELESS TREASURE (Sol-fa, 0/6)	1/0	—	—
JESUS, NOW WILL WE PRAISE THEE	1/0	—	—
JESUS SLEEPS, WHAT HOPE REMAINETH	1/0	—	—
MAGNIFICAT, IN D	1/0	—	—
MASS, IN B MINOR (Choruses only, Sol-fa, 2/0)	2/6	3/0	4/0
MISSA BREVIS, IN A	1/6	—	—
MY SPIRIT WAS IN HEAVINESS (Sol-fa, 0/8)	1/0	—	—
NOW SHALL THE GRACE (Sol-fa, 0/6)	0/6	—	—
O LIGHT EVERLASTING (Sol-fa, 0/8)	1/0	—	—
O TEACH ME, LORD, MY DAYS TO NUMBER	1/0	—	—
PRAISE OUR GOD WHO REIGNS IN HEAVEN	1/0	—	—
PRAISE THOU THE LORD, JERUSALEM	1/0	—	—
J. S. BACH (continued).			
SING YE TO THE LORD (Motet) (Sol-fa, 1/0)	1/0	—	—
SLEEPERS, WAKE (Sol-fa, 0/6)	1/0	—	—
STRIKE, THOU HOUR SO LONG EXPECTED	1/0	—	—
THE LORD IS A SUN AND SHIELD	1/0	—	—
THE LORD IS MY SHEPHERD	1/0	—	—
THE PASSION (S. John)	2/0	2/6	4/0
THE PASSION (S. Matthew)	2/6	3/0	—
DITTO (Abridged, as used at St. Paul's)	1/6	2/0	—
(DITTO. CHORUSES ONLY (Sol-fa, 1/0))			
THE SAGES OF SHEBA	1/0	—	—
THE SPIRIT ALSO HELPETH US (Motet)	1/0	—	—
THERE IS NOUGHT OF SOUNDNESS	1/0	—	—
THOU GUIDE OF ISRAEL	1/0	—	—
WATCH YE, PRAY YE	1/0	—	—
WHEN WILL GOD RECALL MY SPIRIT	1/0	—	—
A. S. BAKER.			
COMMUNION SERVICE, IN E	1/6	—	—
GRANVILLE BANTOCK.			
THE FIRE-WORSHIPPERS	2/6	—	—
J. BARNBY.			
KING ALL GLORIOUS (Sol-fa, 0/1½)	0/6	—	—
REBEKAH (Sol-fa, 0/9)	1/0	1/6	2/6
THE LORD IS KING (97th Psalm) (Sol-fa, 1/0)	1/6	2/0	—
LEONARD BARNES.			
THE BRIDAL DAY	2/6	—	4/6
J. F. BARNETT.			
ANCIENT MARINER (Sol-fa, 2/0)	3/6	4/0	5/0
PARADISE AND THE PERI	4/0	—	6/0
RAISING OF LAZARUS	6/6	—	9/0
THE WISHING BELL (Female voices) (Sol-fa, 1/0)	2/6	—	—
MARMADUKE BARTON.			
MASS IN A MAJOR (For Advent and Lent)	1/0	—	—
ARNOLD BAX.			
FATHERLAND	1/0	—	—
BEETHOVEN.			
A CALM SEA AND A PROSPEROUS VOYAGE	0/4	—	—
CHORAL FANTASIA (Sol-fa, 0/3)	1/0	—	—
CHORAL SYMPHONY	2/6	—	—
DITTO VOCAL PORTION (Sol-fa, 0/6)	1/6	—	—
COMMUNION SERVICE, IN C	1/6	—	3/0
ENGEDI; OR, DAVID IN THE WILDERNESS	1/0	1/6	2/6
MASS, IN C	1/0	1/6	2/6
MASS, IN D	2/0	2/6	4/0
MOUNT OF OLIVES (Choruses, Sol-fa, 0/6)	1/0	1/6	2/6
DITTO CHORUSES ONLY	0/6	1/0	—
PRAISE OF MUSIC	1/6	2/0	3/0
RUINS OF ATHENS (Sol-fa, 0/6)	1/6	—	—
A. H. BEHREND.			
SINGERS FROM THE SEA (Female Voices) (Ditto, Sol-fa, 0/9)	1/6	—	—
THROUGH THE YEAR (Female Voices) (Sol-fa, 0/9)	2/0	—	—
WILFRED BENDALL.			
A LEGEND OF BREGENZ (Female voices) (Ditto, Sol-fa, 0/8)	1/6	—	—
SONG DANCES. Vocal Suite. (Female Voices) (Ditto, Sol-fa, 0/8)	1/0	—	—
THE LADY OF SHALOTT (Female voices) (Ditto, Sol-fa, 0/8)	1/6	—	—
KAREL BENDL.			
WATER-SPRITE'S REVENGE (Female voices)	1/0	—	—
SIR JULIUS BENEDICT.			
LEGEND OF ST. CECILIA (Sol-fa, 1/3)	2/6	3/0	4/0
PASSION MUSIC (from St. Peter)	1/6	—	—
ST. PETER	3/0	3/6	5/0
GEORGE J. BENNETT.			
EASTER HYMN	1/0	—	—
SIR W. STERNDALE BENNETT.			
INTERNATIONAL EXHIBITION ODE (1862)	1/0	—	—
THE MAY QUEEN (Sol-fa, 0/6)	1/0	1/6	2/6
DITTO CHORUSES ONLY (Sol-fa, 1/0)	0/8	1/2	—
THE WOMAN OF SAMARIA (Sol-fa, 1/0)	4/0	—	6/0

Most of these Cantatas, &c., can be supplied in Roan, rounded corners, red under gilt edges, price 3s. in excess of the marked price of the paper cover edition.

HECTOR BERLIOZ.

	Paper Cover.	Paper Boards.	Cloth Gilt.
CHILDHOOD OF CHRIST	2/0	—	—
(DITTO CHORUSES AND WORDS OF SOLOS ONLY, SOL-FA, 0/8)			
FAUST	2/6	—	—
(DITTO CHORUSES AND WORDS OF SOLOS ONLY, SOL-FA, 1/0)			
TE DEUM LAUDAMUS (Latin) (SOL-FA, 1/6)	2/0	—	—

G. R. BETJEMANN.

THE SONG OF THE WESTERN MEN	1/0	—	—

W. R. BEXFIELD.

ISRAEL RESTORED	4/0	—	—

HUGH BLAIR.

BLESSED ARE THEY WHO WATCH (ADVENT)	1/6	—	—
HARVEST-TIDE	1/0	—	—
THE SONG OF DEBORAH AND BARAK	2/6	—	—
TRAFALGAR (SOL-FA, 0/8)	1/6	—	—

JOSIAH BOOTH.

THE DAY OF REST (Female voices) (SOL-FA, 0/9)	1/6	—	—

RUTLAND BOUGHTON.

MIDNIGHT	2/0	—	—
THE INVINCIBLE ARMADA	1/6	—	—
THE SKELETON IN ARMOUR	2/0	—	—

KATE BOUNDY.

THE RIVAL FLOWERS (Operetta) (SOL-FA, 0/6)	1/6	—	—

E. M. BOYCE.

THE LAY OF THE BROWN ROSARY	1/6	—	—
THE SANDS OF CORRIEMIE (Female voices)	1/6	—	—
(DITTO, SOL-FA, 0/6)			
YOUNG LOCHINVAR	1/6	—	—

J. BRADFORD.

HARVEST CANTATA	1/6	—	—

J. BRAHMS.

A SONG OF DESTINY	1/0	—	—

C. BRAUN.

COUNTRY MOUSE AND THE TOWN MOUSE (Operetta) (SOL-FA, 0/4)	1/0	—	—
QUEEN MAB AND THE KOBOLDS (Operetta) (SOL-FA, 0/9)	2/0	—	—
SIGURD	5/0	—	—
SNOW QUEEN (Operetta) (SOL-FA, 0/6)	1/0	—	—

A. HERBERT BREWER.

EMMAUS (SOL-FA, 0/9)	1/6	2/0	—
HOLY INNOCENTS	2/0	—	—
O PRAISE THE LORD	1/0	—	—
O SING UNTO THE LORD (98th Psalm)	1/6	—	—
SIR PATRICK SPENS (Ballad) (SOL-FA, 0/8)	1/6	—	—
SONG OF EDEN	1/0	—	—

J. C. BRIDGE.

DANIEL	3/6	—	—
RESURGAM	1/6	—	—
RUDEL	4/0	—	—

J. F. BRIDGE.

BALLAD OF THE CLAMPHERDOWN	1/0	—	—
(DITTO, SOL-FA, 0/8)			
BOADICEA	2/6	—	—
CALLIRHOË (SOL-FA, 1/6)	2/6	3/0	4/0
CRADLE OF CHRIST ("Stabat Mater Speciosa")	1/6	—	—
FLAG OF ENGLAND (SOL-FA, 0/9)	1/6	—	—
FORGING THE ANCHOR (SOL-FA, 1/0)	1/6	—	—
FROGS AND THE OX (Operetta) (SOL-FA, 0/6)	1/0	—	—
HYMN TO THE CREATOR	1/0	—	—
INCHCAPE ROCK (SOL-FA, 0/6)	1/0	—	—
LOBSTER'S GARDEN PARTY (Female vv.)	1/0	—	—
(DITTO, SOL-FA, 0/4)			
LORD'S PRAYER (SOL-FA, 0/6)	1/0	—	—
MOUNT MORIAH	3/0	—	—
NINEVEH	2/6	3/0	4/0
ROCK OF AGES (Latin and English) (SOL-FA, 0/4)	1/0	—	—
SPIDER AND THE FLY (Operetta) (SOL-FA, 0/6)	1/0	—	—

DUDLEY BUCK.

THE LIGHT OF ASIA	3/0	3/6	5/0

EDWARD BUNNETT.

OUT OF THE DEEP (130th Psalm)	1/0	—	—

T. A. BURTON.

CAPTAIN REECE (Boys' voices) (SOL-FA, 0/6)	1/0	—	—
THE MARTINET. Humorous Naval Cantata for Boys (SOL-FA, 0/6)	1/0	—	—
THE TRAGEDY OF COCK ROBIN (Short Action Piece) (SOL-FA, 0/3)	0/8	—	—
THE YARN OF THE NANCY BELL (Cantata or School Song) (Boys' voices) (SOL-FA, 0/6)	1/0	—	—

W. BYRD.

MASS FOR FOUR VOICES	2/6	—	—

CARISSIMI.

JEPHTHAH	1/0	—	—

A. VON AHN CARSE.

THE LAY OF THE BROWN ROSARY	2/6	—	—

WILLIAM CARTER.

PLACIDA (CHORUSES ONLY, 1/0)	2/0	2/6	4/0

CHERUBINI.

FIRST REQUIEM MASS, C MINOR (Lat. and Eng.)	1/0	1/6	2/6
SECOND MASS, IN D MINOR	2/0	2/6	3/6
THIRD MASS (Coronation)	1/0	1/6	2/6
FOURTH MASS, IN C	1/0	1/6	2/6

E. T. CHIPP.

JOB	4/0	—	—
NAOMI	2/0	—	—

HAMILTON CLARKE.

DAISY CHAIN (Operetta) (SOL-FA, 0/9)	2/6	—	—
DRUMS AND VOICES (Operetta) (SOL-FA, 0/9)	2/0	—	—
HORNPIPE HARRY (Operetta) (SOL-FA, 0/9)	2/6	—	—
MISSING DUKE (Operetta) (SOL-FA, 0/9)	2/6	—	—
PEPIN THE PIPPIN (Operetta) (SOL-FA, 0/9)	2/6	—	—

FREDERIC CLIFFE.

THE NORTH-EAST WIND (SOL-FA, 0/9)	2/0	2/6	—

GERARD F. COBB.

A SONG OF TRAFALGAR (Men's voices)	2/0	—	—
MY SOUL TRULY WAITETH	1/0	—	—

S. COLERIDGE-TAYLOR.

ATONEMENT	3/6	4/0	5/0
BLIND GIRL OF CASTÉL-CUILLÉ	2/6	3/0	—
(DITTO, SOL-FA, 1/0)			
BON-BON SUITE (SOL-FA, 1/0)	2/0	—	—
DEATH OF MINNEHAHA (SOL-FA, 1/0)	1/6	—	—
HIAWATHA'S WEDDING-FEAST (SOL-FA, 1/0)	1/6	—	—
HIAWATHA'S HOCHZEIT	3 mark		
HIAWATHA'S DEPARTURE (SOL-FA, 1/0)	2/0	—	—
MEG BLANE (SOL-FA, 0/9)	2/0	—	—
SCENES FROM THE SONG OF HIAWATHA	3/6	4/0	5/0
(DITTO, SOL-FA, 1/0)			

FREDERICK CORDER.

THE BRIDAL OF TRIERMAIN (SOL-FA, 1/0)	2/6	—	—

SIR MICHAEL COSTA.

THE DREAM	1/0	—	—

H. COWARD.

GARETH AND LINET (SOL-FA, Choruses only, 1/0)	2/6	—	—
THE STORY OF BETHANY (SOL-FA, 1/6)	2/6	3/0	—

F. H. COWEN.

CHRISTMAS SCENES (Female voices) (SOL-FA, 0/9)	2/0	—	—
CORONATION ODE	1/6	—	—
DAUGHTER OF THE SEA (Female vv.) (SOL-FA, 1/0)	2/0	—	—
HE GIVETH HIS BELOVED SLEEP (SOL-FA, 0/6)	1/0	—	—
JOHN GILPIN (SOL-FA, 1/0)	2/0	—	—
ODE TO THE PASSIONS (SOL-FA, 1/0)	2/0	—	—
ROSE OF LIFE (Female voices) (SOL-FA, 0/9)	2/0	—	—
RUTH (SOL-FA, 1/6)	4/0	4/6	6/0
SLEEPING BEAUTY (SOL-FA, 1/6)	2/6	3/0	4/0
SONG OF THANKSGIVING	1/6	—	—
ST. JOHN'S EVE (SOL-FA, 1/6)	2/6	3/0	4/0
SUMMER ON THE RIVER (Female vv.) (SOL-FA, 0/9)	2/0	—	—
THORGRIM (Opera)	5/0	—	7/6
VILLAGE SCENES (Female voices) (SOL-FA, 0/9)	1/6	—	—
WATER LILY	1/6	—	—

J. W. COWIE.

VIA CRUCIS (SOL-FA, 1/0)	1/6	—	—

J. MAUDE CRAMENT.

I WILL MAGNIFY THEE, O GOD (145th Psalm)	2/6	—	—
LITTLE RED RIDING-HOOD (Female voices)	2/0	—	—

W. CRESER.

EUDORA (A dramatic Idyll)	2/6	—	—

W. CROTCH.

PALESTINE	3/0	3/6	5/0

W. H. CUMMINGS.

THE FAIRY RING	2/6	—	—

W. G. CUSINS.

TE DEUM, IN B FLAT	1/6	—	—

FÉLICIEN DAVID.

THE DESERT (Male voices) (SOL-FA, 0/8)	1/6	2/0	3/0

W. T. DAVID.

THE BLIND MAN OF JUDAH (SOL-FA, 1/0)	2/0	2/6	—

H. WALFORD DAVIES.

EVERYMAN (founded upon the old Morality play)	3/0	4/0	—
(SOL-FA, 2/0)			
HERVÉ RIEL	1/0	—	—
HUMPTY-DUMPTY (for Children) (SOL-FA, 0/9)	1/6	—	—
LIFT UP YOUR HEARTS (Sacred Symphony)	2/6	—	—
NOBLE NUMBERS	3/0	—	—
ODE ON TIME	1/0	—	—
THE THREE JOVIAL HUNTSMEN (Folio)	1/6	—	—
THE TEMPLE (Oratorio)	4/0	5/0	6/0

P. H. DEIMER.

	Paper Cover	Paper Boards	Cloth Gilt
BETHANY	4/0	—	—

F. G. DOSSERT.

	Paper Cover	Paper Boards	Cloth Gilt
COMMUNION SERVICE, IN E MINOR	2/0	—	—
MASS, IN E MINOR	5/0	—	—

LUCY K. DOWNING.

	Paper Cover	Paper Boards	Cloth Gilt
A PARABLE IN SONG	2/0	—	—

T. F. DUNHILL.

	Paper Cover	Paper Boards	Cloth Gilt
THE FROLICSOME HOURS (Musical Fantasy) (DITTO, SOL-FA, 0/6.)	1/6	—	—
TUBAL CAIN (Ballad) (SOL-FA, 0/6)	1/0	—	—

F. DUNKLEY.

	Paper Cover	Paper Boards	Cloth Gilt
THE WRECK OF THE HESPERUS	1/0	—	—

ANTONIN DVOŘÁK.

	Paper Cover	Paper Boards	Cloth Gilt
AT THE FOOT OF THE CROSS (Stabat Mater) (SOL-FA, 1/6)	2/6	3/0	4/0
COMMUNION SERVICE, IN D	1/6	—	—
MASS, IN D	1/6	—	—
PATRIOTIC HYMN	1/6	—	—
DITTO (German and Bohemian Words)	3/0	—	—
REQUIEM MASS	5/0	6/0	7/6
SPECTRE'S BRIDE (SOL-FA, 1/6)	3/0	3/6	5/0
DITTO (German and Bohemian Words)	6/0	—	—
ST. LUDMILA	5/0	6/0	7/6
DITTO (German and Bohemian Words)	8/0	—	—
STABAT MATER (Latin only) (SOL-FA, 1/6)	2/6	3/0	4/0

A. E. DYER.

	Paper Cover	Paper Boards	Cloth Gilt
ELECTRA OF SOPHOCLES	1/6	2/0	—
SALVATOR MUNDI	2/6	—	—

JOHN B. DYKES.

	Paper Cover	Paper Boards	Cloth Gilt
THE LORD IS MY SHEPHERD	1/0	—	—
THESE ARE THEY (SOL-FA, 0/2)	0/6	—	—

H. J. EDWARDS.

	Paper Cover	Paper Boards	Cloth Gilt
PRAISE TO THE HOLIEST	1/6	—	—
THE ASCENSION	2/6	—	—
THE EPIPHANY	2/0	—	—
THE RISEN LORD	2/6	—	—

EDWARD ELGAR.

	Paper Cover	Paper Boards	Cloth Gilt
APOSTLES (Oratorio) (DITTO, Choruses and Words of Solos only, SOL-FA, 2/6) (DITTO, German Words, 8 Mark)	5/0	6/0	7/6
BANNER OF ST. GEORGE (SOL-FA 1/0)	1/6	—	—
BLACK KNIGHT (SOL-FA, 1/0)	2/0	—	—
CARACTACUS (SOL-FA, Choruses only, 1/6)	3/6	4/0	5/0
DREAM OF GERONTIUS (DITTO, SOL-FA, Choruses only, 1/6) (DITTO, French Words, Prix fr. 7.50 net) (DITTO, German Words, 6 Mark)	3/6	4/0	5/0
GO, SONG OF MINE (Chorus, Six-part) (SOLFA, 0/3)	0/6	—	—
KINGDOM (Oratorio) (DITTO, Choruses and Words of Solos only, SOL-FA, 2/6) (DITTO, German Words, 5 mark)	5/0	6/0	7/6
KING OLAF (SOL-FA, Choruses only, 1/6)	3/0	3/6	5/0
LIGHT OF LIFE (Lux Christi) (SOL-FA, 1/0)	2/6	—	—
TE DEUM AND BENEDICTUS	1/0	—	—

ROSALIND F. ELLICOTT.

	Paper Cover	Paper Boards	Cloth Gilt
ELYSIUM	1/0	—	—
THE BIRTH OF SONG	1/6	—	—

GUSTAV ERNEST.

	Paper Cover	Paper Boards	Cloth Gilt
ALL THE YEAR ROUND (Female vv.) (SOL-FA, 0/9)	1/6	—	—

HARRY EVANS.

	Paper Cover	Paper Boards	Cloth Gilt
THE VICTORY OF ST. GARMON (SOL-FA, 0/9)	1/6	—	—

A. J. EYRE.

	Paper Cover	Paper Boards	Cloth Gilt
COMMUNION SERVICE IN E FLAT	1/0	—	—

T. FACER.

	Paper Cover	Paper Boards	Cloth Gilt
A MERRY CHRISTMAS (School Cantata) (DITTO, SOL-FA, 0/6)	1/0	—	—
RED RIDING-HOOD'S RECEPTION (Operetta) (DITTO, SOL-FA, 0/9)	2/6	—	—
SONS OF THE EMPIRE (School Cantata) (DITTO, SOL-FA 0/6)	1/6	—	—

E. FANING.

	Paper Cover	Paper Boards	Cloth Gilt
BUTTERCUPS AND DAISIES (Female voices) (DITTO, SOL-FA, 0/9)	1/6	—	—

HENRY FARMER.

	Paper Cover	Paper Boards	Cloth Gilt
MASS, IN B FLAT (Latin and English) (SOL-FA, 1/0)	2/0	2/6	3/6

PERCY E. FLETCHER.

	Paper Cover	Paper Boards	Cloth Gilt
THE ENCHANTED ISLAND (Operetta) (DITTO, SOL-FA, 0/9)	2/0	—	—
THE OLD YEAR'S VISION (Operetta) (SOL-FA, 0/6)	1/6	—	—
THE TOY REVIEW (Operetta) (SOL-FA, 0/8)	1/6	—	—

J. C. FORRESTER.

	Paper Cover	Paper Boards	Cloth Gilt
THE KALENDAR (Operetta) (SOL-FA, 0/9)	2/0	—	—

MYLES B. FOSTER.

	Paper Cover	Paper Boards	Cloth Gilt
ANGELS OF THE BELLS (Female voices) (DITTO, SOL-FA, 0/8)	1/6	—	—
BONNIE FISHWIVES (Female vv.) (SOL-FA, 0/9)	1/6	—	—
COMING OF THE KING (Female voices) (DITTO, SOL-FA, 0/8)	1/6	—	—
SNOW FAIRIES (Female voices) (SOL-FA, 0/6)	1/6	—	—

ROBERT FRANZ.

	Paper Cover	Paper Boards	Cloth Gilt
PRAISE YE THE LORD (117th Psalm)	1/0	—	—

A. M. FRIEDLÄNDER.

	Paper Cover	Paper Boards	Cloth Gilt
MUSIC (An Ode)	1/6	—	—
THE RETURN TO ZION	2/6	—	—

NIELS W. GADE.

	Paper Cover	Paper Boards	Cloth Gilt
CHRISTMAS EVE (SOL-FA, 0/4)	1/0	1/6	—
COMALA	2/0	2/6	4/0
CRUSADERS (SOL-FA, 1/0)	2/0	2/6	4/0
ERL-KING'S DAUGHTER (SOL-FA, 0/9)	1/0	1/6	2/6
PSYCHE (SOL-FA, 1/6)	2/6	3/0	4/0
SPRING'S MESSAGE (SOL-FA, 0/3)	0/8	—	—
ZION	1/0	1/6	2/6

HENRY GADSBY.

	Paper Cover	Paper Boards	Cloth Gilt
ALCESTIS (Male voices)	4/0	—	—
COLUMBUS (Male voices)	2/6	—	—
LORD OF THE ISLES (SOL-FA, 1/6)	2/6	—	—

F. W. GALPIN.

	Paper Cover	Paper Boards	Cloth Gilt
YE OLDE ENGLYSHE PASTYMES (Female voices)	1/6	—	—

G. GARRETT.

	Paper Cover	Paper Boards	Cloth Gilt
HARVEST CANTATA (SOL-FA, 0/6)	1/0	—	—
THE SHUNAMMITE	3/0	—	—
THE TWO ADVENTS	1/6	—	—

R. MACHILL GARTH.

	Paper Cover	Paper Boards	Cloth Gilt
EZEKIEL	4/0	—	—
THE WILD HUNTSMAN	1/0	1/6	—

A. R. GAUL.

	Paper Cover	Paper Boards	Cloth Gilt
AROUND THE WINTER FIRE (Female voices) (DITTO, SOL-FA, 0/9)	2/0	—	—
A SONG OF LIFE (Ode to Music) (SOL-FA, 0/6)	1/0	—	—
ELFIN HILL (Female voices)	2/0	—	—
HARE AND THE TORTOISE (SOL-FA, 0/6)	1/0	—	—
HOLY CITY (SOL-FA, 1/0)	2/6	3/0	4/0
ISRAEL IN THE WILDERNESS (SOL-FA, 1/0)	2/6	3/0	4/0
JOAN OF ARC (SOL-FA, 1/0)	2/6	3/0	4/0
LEGEND OF THE WOOD (Female) (SOL-FA, 0/8)	1/0	—	—
PASSION SERVICE	2/6	3/0	4/0
PRINCE OF PEACE (SOL-FA, 1/0)	2/6	3/0	4/0
RUTH (SOL-FA, 0/9) (Choruses only, 1/0)	2/0	2/6	4/0
TEN VIRGINS (SOL-FA, 1/0)	2/6	3/0	4/0
TOILERS OF THE DEEP (Female voices)	2/0	—	—
UNA (SOL-FA, 1/0)	2/6	3/0	4/0
UNION JACK (Unison Song with Actions)	0/6	—	—

FR. GERNSHEIM.

	Paper Cover	Paper Boards	Cloth Gilt
SALAMIS. A TRIUMPH SONG (Male voices)	1/0	—	—

E. OUSELEY GILBERT.

	Paper Cover	Paper Boards	Cloth Gilt
SANTA CLAUS AND HIS COMRADES (Operetta) (DITTO, SOL-FA, 0/8)	2/0	—	—

F. E. GLADSTONE.

	Paper Cover	Paper Boards	Cloth Gilt
PHILIPPI	2/6	—	—

GLUCK.

	Paper Cover	Paper Boards	Cloth Gilt
ORPHEUS (CHORUSES, SOL-FA, 1/0)	3/6	—	—
DITTO (ACT II. ONLY)	1/6	—	—

PERCY GODFREY.

	Paper Cover	Paper Boards	Cloth Gilt
THE SONG OF THE AMAL	1/6	—	—

HERMANN GOETZ.

	Paper Cover	Paper Boards	Cloth Gilt
BY THE WATERS OF BABYLON (137th Psalm)	1/0	—	—
NOENIA	1/0	—	—
THE WATER-LILY (Male voices) (SOL-FA, 0/9)	1/6	—	—

A. M. GOODHART.

	Paper Cover	Paper Boards	Cloth Gilt
ARETHUSA	1/0	—	—
EARL HALDAN'S DAUGHTER	1/0	—	—
FOUNDER'S DAY (Ode)	1/6	—	—
SIR ANDREW BARTON	1/0	—	—
THE SPANISH ARMADA	0/6	—	—

CH. GOUNOD.

	Paper Cover	Paper Boards	Cloth Gilt
COMMUNION SERVICE (Messe Solennelle)	1/6	2/0	3/0
DITTO (Troisième Messe Solennelle)	1/6	—	—
DAUGHTERS OF JERUSALEM (Latin, 1/0)	1/0	—	—
DE PROFUNDIS (English or Latin Words)	1/0	—	—
FAUST (Selection) (SOL-FA, 0/9)	1/0	—	—
GALLIA (SOL-FA, 0/4)	1/0	—	—
MESSE SOLENNELLE (ST. CECILIA)	1/0	1/6	2/6
MESSE SOLENNELLE (Troisième)	1/6	—	—
MORS ET VITA (Latin or English Words)	2/6	3/0	5/0
DITTO SOL-FA (Latin and English Words)	1/0	—	—
DITTO Parts II. and III.	1/6	—	—
DITTO Parts II. and III. (English Words)	1/6	—	—
DITTO REQUIEM MASS	1/6	2/0	—
O COME NEAR TO THE CROSS (Stabat Mater)	0/8	—	—
OUT OF DARKNESS	1/0	—	—
THE REDEMPTION (English Words) (SOL-FA, 1/0)	2/6	3/0	5/0
DITTO (French Words)	8/4	—	—
DITTO (German Words)	10/0	—	—
DITTO Part I.	1/6	—	—
DITTO Parts II. and III. each	1/0	—	—

C. H. GRAUN.

	Paper Cover.	Paper Boards.	Cloth Gilt.
TE DEUM	2/0	2/6	4/0
THE PASSION OF OUR LORD (Der Tod Jesu)	2/0	2/6	4/0
(CHORUSES ONLY, 1/0)			

ALAN GRAY.

ARETHUSA	1/6	—	—
A SONG OF REDEMPTION	1/6	—	—
THE LEGEND OF THE ROCK-BUOY BELL	1/0	—	—
THE WIDOW OF ZAREPHATH	2/0	—	—

J. O. GRIMM.

THE SOUL'S ASPIRATION	1/0	—	—

G. HALFORD.

THE PARACLETE	2/0	—	—

E. V. HALL.

IS IT NOTHING TO YOU (SOL-FA, 0/3)	0/8	—	—

W. A. HALL.

THE PRESENTATION IN THE TEMPLE	1/6	—	—

HANDEL.

ACIS AND GALATEA	1/0	1/6	2/6
Ditto, New Edition, edited by J. Barnby (SOL-FA, 0/9)	1/0	1/6	2/6
ALCESTE	2/0	—	—
ALEXANDER BALUS	3/0	3/6	5/0
ALEXANDER'S FEAST	2/0	2/6	4 0
ATHALIAH	3/0	3/6	5/0
BELSHAZZAR	3/0	3/6	5/0
CHANDOS TE DEUM	1/0	1/6	2/6
CORONATION AND FUNERAL ANTHEMS	—	—	5/0
Or, singly:—			
LET THY HAND BE STRENGTHENED	0/6	—	—
MY HEART IS INDITING	0/8	—	—
THE KING SHALL REJOICE (SOL-FA, 0/3)	0/6	—	—
THE WAYS OF ZION	1/0	—	—
ZADOK THE PRIEST (SOL-FA, 0/1½)	0/3	—	—
DEBORAH	2/0	2/6	4/0
DETTINGEN TE DEUM	1/0	1/6	2/6
DIXIT DOMINUS (from Psalm cx.)	1/0	—	—
ESTHER	3/0	3/6	5/0
HERCULES (CHORUSES ONLY, 1/0)	3/0	3/6	5/0
ISRAEL IN EGYPT, edited by Mendelssohn	2/0	2/6	4/0
ISRAEL IN EGYPT, edited by V. Novello, Pocket Edit.	1/0	1/6	2/0
(DITTO, SOL-FA, 1/0)			
JEPHTHA	2/0	2/6	4/0
JOSHUA	2/0	2/6	4/0
JUDAS MACCABÆUS (SOL-FA, 1/0)	2/0	2/6	4/0
JUDAS MACCABÆUS, Pocket Edition	1/0	1/6	2/0
Ditto (CHORUSES ONLY)	0/8	1/2	—
Ditto New Edition. Edited by John E. West	2/0	—	—
L'ALLEGRO (CHORUSES ONLY, 1/0)	2/0	2/6	4/0
NISI DOMINUS	1/0	—	—
O COME, LET US SING (5th Chandos Anthem)	1/0	—	—
ODE ON ST. CECILIA'S DAY	1/0	1/6	2/6
O PRAISE THE LORD (6th Chandos) (SOL-FA, 0/4)	1/0	—	—
O PRAISE THE LORD, YE ANGELS (Folio)	2/6	—	—
SAMSON (SOL-FA, 1/0)	2/0	2/6	4/0
Ditto (CHORUSES ONLY)	0/8	1/2	—
SAUL (CHORUSES ONLY, 1/0)	2/0	2/6	4/0
SEMELE	3/0	3/6	5/0
SOLOMON (CHORUSES ONLY, 1/6)	2/0	2/6	4/0
SUSANNA	3/0	3/6	5/0
THEODORA	3/0	3/6	5/0
THE MESSIAH, edited by V. Novello (SOL-FA 1/0)	2/0	2/6	4/0
THE MESSIAH, edited by E. Prout (SOL-FA, 1/0)	2/0	2/6	4/0
THE MESSIAH, edited by V. Novello, Pocket Edition	1/0	1/6	2/0
THE MESSIAH, edited by W. T. Best (SOL-FA, 1/0)	2/0	2/6	4/0
Ditto (CHORUSES ONLY)	0/8	1/2	—
THE PASSION	3/0	3/6	5/0
Ditto (Abridged Edition)	1/0	—	—
THE TRIUMPH OF TIME AND TRUTH	3/0	3/6	5/0
UTRECHT JUBILATE	1/0	—	—

SYDNEY HARDCASTLE.

SING A SONG OF SIXPENCE (Operetta)	0/6	—	—

T. M. HARDY.

RIP VAN WINKLE (Operetta) (SOL-FA, 0/6)	1/6	—	—

C. A. E. HARRISS.

PAN (A Choric Idyl)	2/6	—	—
THE SANDS OF DEE	1/0	—	—

CHARLES HART-DAVIS.

THE COURT CARD (Musical Sketch for Junior Classes) (SOL-FA, 0/6)	1/6	—	—

BASIL HARWOOD.

AS BY THE STREAMS OF BABYLON	1/6	—	—
INCLINA, DOMINE (86th Psalm)	3/0	—	—
JESUS! THY BOUNDLESS LOVE TO ME	1/0	—	—

J. W. G. HATHAWAY.

A LEGEND OF BREGENZ	1/6	—	—
HOW SWEET THE MOONLIGHT SLEEPS	1/0	—	—
JACK HORNER'S RIDE (for Children)	2/0	—	—
(SOL-FA, 0/8)			

F. K. HATTERSLEY.

HOW THEY BROUGHT THE GOOD NEWS FROM GHENT TO AIX	1/6	—	—
KING ROBERT OF SICILY	2/6	—	—

HAYDN.

	Paper Cover.	Paper Boards.	Cloth Gilt.
CREATION (SOL-FA, 1/0)	2/0	2/6	4/0
CREATION, Pocket Edition	1/0	1/6	2/0
Ditto (CHORUSES ONLY)	0/8	1/2	—
INSANÆ ET VANÆ CURÆ (Latin or English)	0/4	—	—
MASS, IN B FLAT, No. 1 (Latin)	1/0	1/6	2/6
Ditto (Latin and English)	1/0	1/6	2/6
MASS, IN C, No. 2 (Latin)	1/0	1/6	2/6
MASS, IN D, No. 3 (IMPERIAL) (Latin and English)	1/0	1/6	2/6
Ditto (Latin)	1/0	1/6	2/6
MASS, IN B FLAT, No. 16 (Latin)	1/6	2/0	3/0
PASSION; OR, SEVEN LAST WORDS	2/0	2/6	4/0
SEASONS (complete)	3/0	3/6	5/0
Each Season, singly (SPRING, Tonic Sol-fa, 6d.)	1/0	—	—
Ditto (CHORUSES ONLY)	1/0	1/6	—
TE DEUM (English and Latin)	1/0	—	—

BATTISON HAYNES.

A SEA DREAM (Female voices) (SOL-FA, 0/6)	1/6	—	—
THE FAIRIES' ISLE (Female voices)	1/6	—	—
THE SEA FAIRIES (Female voices) (SOL-FA 0/6)	1/6	—	—

C. SWINNERTON HEAP.

FAIR ROSAMOND (SOL-FA, 2/0)	3/6	4/0	5/0
Ditto (CHORUSES ONLY)	1/6	—	—

EDWARD HECHT.

ERIC THE DANE	3/0	—	—
O MAY I JOIN THE CHOIR INVISIBLE	1/0	—	—

GEORG HENSCHEL.

OUT OF DARKNESS (130th Psalm)	2/6	—	—
STABAT MATER	2/6	—	—
TE DEUM LAUDAMUS, IN C	1/6	—	—

H. M. HIGGS.

THE ERL KING	1/0	—	—

HENRY HILES.

GOD IS OUR REFUGE	0/6	—	—
THE CRUSADERS	2/6	—	—
WAR IN THE HOUSEHOLD	2/0	—	—

FERDINAND HILLER.

ALL THEY THAT TRUST IN THEE	0/8	—	—
A SONG OF VICTORY (SOL-FA 0/9)	1/0	1/6	—
NALA AND DAMAYANTI	4/0	—	6/0

H. E. HODSON.

THE GOLDEN LEGEND	2/0	—	—

HEINRICH HOFMANN.

CHAMPAGNERLIED (Male voices)	1/6	—	—
CINDERELLA	2/6	—	—
MELUSINA	2/0	2/6	4/0
SONG OF THE NORNS (Female voices)	1/0	—	—

SIDNEY R. HOGG.

THE NORMAN BARON	1/6	—	—

JOSEPH HOLBROOKE.

BYRON (Poem)	1/6	—	—

C. HOLLAND.

AFTER THE SKIRMISH	1/0	—	—

T. S. HOLLAND.

A PASTORAL MEDLEY (Musical Sketch) (SOL-FA, 0/9)	2/0	—	—
KING GOLDEMAR (Operetta) (SOL-FA, 0/9)	2/0	—	—

GUSTAV VON HOLST.

KING ESTMERE (Ballad)	2/0	—	—
THE IDEA (Humorous Operetta) (SOL-FA, 0/6)	1/0	—	—

HUMMEL.

ALMA VIRGO (Latin and English)	0/4	—	—
COMMUNION SERVICE, IN B FLAT	2/0	—	4/0
Ditto, IN E FLAT	2/0	—	4 0
Ditto, IN D	2/0	—	4/0
MASS, IN B FLAT, No. 1	1/0	1/6	2/6
MASS, IN E FLAT, No. 2	1/0	1/6	2/6
MASS, IN D, No. 3	1/0	1/6	2/6
QUOD IN ORBE (Latin and English)	0/4	—	—

W. H. HUNT.

STABAT MATER	1/0	1/6	—

G. F. HUNTLEY.

PUSS-IN-BOOTS (Operetta) (SOL-FA, 0/9)	2/0	—	—
VICTORIA	2/0	—	—
(DITTO, SOL-FA, 1/0)			

H. H. HUSS.

AVE MARIA (Female voices)	1/0	—	—

F. ILIFFE.

SWEET ECHO	1/0	—	—

JOHN W. IVIMEY.

WITCH OF THE WOOD (Operetta) (SOL-FA, 0/9)	2/0	—	—

W. JACKSON.

THE YEAR	2/0	2/6	—

G. JACOBI.

	Paper Cover.	Paper Boards.	Cloth Gilt.
CINDERELLA (Operetta) (Sol-fa, 1/0)	2/0	—	—
THE BABES IN THE WOOD (Operetta) (Sol-fa, 0/9)	2/0	—	—

D. JENKINS.

DAVID AND SAUL (Sol-fa, 2/0)	3/0	3/6	—

A. JENSEN.

THE FEAST OF ADONIS (Sol-fa, 0/6)	1/0	1/6	—

W. JOHNSON.

ECCE HOMO	1/0	—	—

H. FESTING JONES.

KING BULBOUS (Operetta) (Sol-fa, 0/8)	2/0	—	—

WARWICK JORDAN.

BLOW YE THE TRUMPET IN ZION	1/0	—	—

N. KILBURN.

BY THE WATERS OF BABYLON	1/0	—	—
THE LORD IS MY SHEPHERD (23rd Psalm)	0/8	—	—
THE SILVER STAR (Female voices)	1/6	—	—

ALFRED KING.

THE EPIPHANY	3/0	—	—

OLIVER KING.

BY THE WATERS OF BABYLON (137th Psalm)	1/6	—	—
THE NAIADS (Female voices)	1/6	—	—
THE ROMANCE OF THE ROSES	2/6	—	—
THE SANDS O' DEE (Ballad) (Sol-fa, 0/2)	0/4	—	—
THE THREE FISHERS (Ballad) (Sol-fa, 0/3)	0/6	—	—

J. KINROSS.

SONGS IN A VINEYARD (Female vv.) (Sol-fa, 0/6)	1/6	—	—

H. LAHEE.

THE SLEEPING BEAUTY (Female vv.) (Sol-fa, 0/6)	1/6	—	—

HENRY LAWES.

THE MASQUE OF COMUS	2/0	—	—

MAX LAISTNER.

THE FRIAR'S MERE (Male Voices)	1/6	—	—

G. F. LE JEUNE.

COMMUNION SERVICE IN C	2/0	—	—
FIRST MASS IN C	2/0	—	—

EDWIN H. LEMARE.

'TIS THE SPRING OF SOULS TO-DAY	1/0	—	—
COMMUNION SERVICE IN F	2/6	—	—

LEONARDO LEO.

DIXIT DOMINUS	1/0	1/6	—

F. LEONI.

THE GATE OF LIFE (Sol-fa, 1/0)	2/0	—	—

H. LESLIE.

THE FIRST CHRISTMAS MORN	2/6	—	—

F. LISZT.

THE LEGEND OF ST. ELIZABETH	3/0	3/6	5/0
THIRTEENTH PSALM	2/0	—	—

C. H. LLOYD.

A HYMN OF THANKSGIVING	2/0	—	—
ALCESTIS (Male voices)	1/6	—	—
ANDROMEDA	3/0	3/6	5/0
A SONG OF JUDGMENT	2/6	3/0	4/0
GLEANERS' HARVEST (Female voices)	1/6	—	—
HERO AND LEANDER	1/6	—	—
LONGBEARDS' SAGA (Male voices)	1/6	—	—
O GIVE THANKS UNTO THE LORD	1/6	—	—
RIGHTEOUS LIVE FOR EVERMORE	1/6	—	—
ROSSALL	2/0	—	—
SIR OGIE AND THE LADIE ELSIE	1/6	—	—
SONG OF BALDER	1/0	—	—

CLEMENT LOCKNANE.

THE ELFIN QUEEN (Female voices)	1/6	—	—

HARVEY LÖHR.

THE QUEEN OF SHEBA (Choruses only, 1/0)	5/0	—	—

W. H. LONGHURST.

THE VILLAGE FAIR (Female Voices)	2/0	2/6	—

ELVA LORENCE AND G. KENNEDY CHRYSTIE.

TERRA FLORA (or a Peep into Flower Land, Operetta for Children)	2/0	—	—

C. EGERTON LOWE.

LITTLE BO-PEEP (Operetta). (Sol-fa, 0/4)	1/0	—	—

HAMISH MacCUNN.

LAY OF THE LAST MINSTREL (Sol-fa, 1/6)	2/6	3/0	4/0
LORD ULLIN'S DAUGHTER (Sol-fa, 0/8)	1/0	—	—
WRECK OF THE HESPERUS (Sol-fa, 0/6)	1/0	—	—

G. A. MACFARREN.

	Paper Cover.	Paper Boards.	Cloth Gilt.
AJAX (Greek Play)	3/0	—	—
MAY-DAY (Sol-fa, 0/6)	1/0	1/6	2/6
Ditto (Choruses only)	0/6	1/0	—
OUTWARD BOUND	1/0	—	2/6
SONGS IN A CORNFIELD (Female voices) (Ditto, Sol-fa, 0/9)	1/6	—	—
ST. JOHN THE BAPTIST (Ditto, Sol-fa, Choruses only, 1/0)	3/0	—	4/0
THE LADY OF THE LAKE (Ditto, Choruses only, Sol-fa, 1/0)	2/0	—	4/0
THE SOLDIER'S LEGACY (Operetta)	6/0	—	—

A. C. MACKENZIE.

BETHLEHEM	5/0	6/0	7/6
Ditto. Act II., separately	2/6	—	—
BRIDE (Sol-fa, 0/8)	1/0	—	—
COLOMBA (Lyrical Drama)	5/0	—	7/6
Ditto (German Words)	8/0	—	10/6
COTTER'S SATURDAY NIGHT (Sol-fa, 1/0)	2/0	—	—
DREAM OF JUBAL (Ditto, Choruses only, Sol-fa, 1/0)	2/6	3/0	4/0
JASON	2/6	3/0	4/0
JUBILEE ODE	1/6	—	—
NEW COVENANT	1/6	—	—
PROCESSION OF THE ARK (Choral Scene) (Ditto, Sol-fa, 0/9)	1/6	—	—
ROSE OF SHARON (Ditto, Sol-fa, 2/0)	5/0	6/0	7/6
STORY OF SAYID	3/0	3/6	5/0
TROUBADOUR (Lyrical Drama)	5/0	—	7/6
VENI, CREATOR SPIRITUS	2/0	—	—
WITCH'S DAUGHTER	3/6	4/0	5/0

A. M. MACLEAN.

THE ANNUNCIATION	2/6	—	—

C. MACPHERSON.

BY THE WATERS OF BABYLON (137th Psalm)	2/0	—	—

L. MANCINELLI.

ERO E LEANDRO (Opera)	5/0	—	—

F. W. MARKULL.

ROLAND'S HORN (Male voices)	2/6	—	—

F. E. MARSHALL.

CHORAL DANCES from Ditto	1/0	—	—
PRINCE SPRITE (Female voices)	2/6	—	—

GEORGE C. MARTIN.

COMMUNION SERVICE, IN A	1/0	—	—
Ditto IN C	1/0	—	—
FESTIVAL TE DEUM IN A (Sol-fa, 0/2)	0/6	—	—

J. MASSENET.

MANON (Opera)	6/0	—	8/0

J. T. MASSER.

HARVEST CANTATA	1/0	—	—

J. H. MAUNDER.

OLIVET TO CALVARY (Sol-fa, 0/9)	1/6	2/0	—
PENITENCE, PARDON, AND PEACE (Sol-fa, 1/0)	1/6	2/0	—
SONG OF THANKSGIVING (Sol-fa, 0/9)	1/6	2/0	—

T. R. MAYOR.

THE LOVE OF CHRIST	1/0	—	—

J. H. MEE.

DELPHI, A LEGEND OF HELLAS (Male voices)	1/0	—	—
HORATIUS (Male voices)	1/0	—	—
MISSA SOLENNIS, IN B FLAT	2/0	—	—

MENDELSSOHN.

ANTIGONE (Male voices) (Sol-fa, 1/0)	4/0	—	—
AS THE HART PANTS (42nd Psalm) (Sol-fa, 0/6)	1/0	—	—
COME, LET US SING (95th Psalm) (Sol-fa, 0/6)	1/0	—	—
NOT UNTO US, O LORD (115th Psalm)	1/0	—	—
WHEN ISRAEL OUT OF EGYPT CAME (Ditto, Sol-fa, 0/9)	1/0	—	—
ATHALIE (Sol-fa, 0/8)	1/0	1/6	4/0
AVE MARIA (Saviour of Sinners) (Double Choir)	1/0	—	—
CHRISTUS (Sol-fa, 0/6)	1/0	—	—
ELIJAH (Pocket Edition)	1/0	1/6	2/0
ELIJAH (Sol-fa, 0/8)	2/0	2/6	4/0
Ditto (Choruses only)	1/0	1/6	—
FESTGESANG (Hymn of Praise) (s.a.t.b.) (Sol-fa, 0/2)	1/0	—	—
Ditto (Male voices) (t.t.b.b.)	1/0	—	—
HEAR MY PRAYER (s. solo and chorus) (Sol-fa, 0/2)	1/0	—	—
Ditto Ditto	0/4	—	—
HYMN OF PRAISE (Lobgesang) (Sol-fa, 0/6)	1/0	1/6	2/6
Ditto (Choruses only)	0/6	1/0	—
JUDGE ME, O GOD (43rd Psalm) (Sol-fa, 0/1½)	0/4	—	—
LAUDA SION (Praise Jehovah) (Sol-fa, 0/9)	1/0	1/6	2/6
LORD, HOW LONG WILT THOU (Sol-fa, 0/4)	1/0	—	—
LORELEY (Sol-fa, 0/6)	1/0	—	—
MAN IS MORTAL (8 voices)	1/0	—	—
MIDSUMMER NIGHT'S DREAM (Female voices) (Ditto, Sol-fa, 0/4)	1/0	—	—
MY GOD, WHY HAST THOU (Sol-fa, 0/4)	0/6	—	—

MENDELSSOHN (*continued*).

	Paper Cover.	Paper Boards.	Cloth Gilt.
ŒDIPUS AT COLONOS (Male voices)	3/0	—	—
ST. PAUL (Sol-fa, 1/0)	2/0	2/6	4/0
Ditto (Choruses only)	1/0	1/6	—
ST. PAUL, Pocket Edition	1/0	1/3	2/0
SING TO THE LORD (98th Psalm)	0/8	—	—
SIX ANTHEMS for the Cathedral at Berlin. For 8 voices, arranged in 4 parts	0/8	—	—
SON AND STRANGER (Operetta)	4/0	—	—
THE FIRST WALPURGIS NIGHT (Sol-fa, 1/0)..	1/0	1/6	2/6
THREE MOTETS FOR FEMALE VOICES	1/0	—	—
(Ditto, Sol-fa, 0/1½, 0/2, and 0/2 each.)			
TO THE SONS OF ART (Male voices) (Sol-fa, 0/3)	1/0	—	—
WHY RAGE FIERCELY THE HEATHEN (Sol-fa, 0/3)	0/6	—	—

R. D. METCALFE and A. KENNEDY.

PRINCE FERDINAND (Operetta) (Sol-fa, 0/9)	2/0	—	—

MEYERBEER.

NINETY-FIRST PSALM (Latin)	1/0	—	—
Ditto (English)	1/0	—	—

A. MOFFAT.

A CHRISTMAS DREAM (A Cantata for Children) (Ditto, Sol-fa, 0/4)	1/0	—	—
THE BEE QUEEN (Operetta) (Sol-fa, 0/6)	1/0	—	—

B. MOLIQUE.

ABRAHAM	3/0	3/6	5/0

J. A. MOONIE.

A WOODLAND DREAM (Female voices) (Sol-fa,0/9)	2/0	—	—
KILLIECRANKIE (Sol-fa, 0/8)	1/6	—	—

HAROLD MOORE.

THE DARKEST HOUR (Sol-fa, 0/9)	1/6	2/0	

MOZART.

COMMUNION SERVICE, IN B FLAT, No. 7	1/6	—	—
GLORY, HONOUR, PRAISE (Sol-fa, 0/2) Third Motet	0/3	—	—
HAVE MERCY, O LORD... Second Motet	0/3	—	—
KING THAMOS	1/0	1/6	—
LITANIA DE VENERABILI ALTARIS (E♭)	1/6	2/0	3/0
LITANIA DE VENERABILI SACRAMENTO (B♭)	1/6	2/0	3/0
MASS IN C, No. 1 (Latin and English)	1/0	1/6	2/6
MASS, IN B FLAT No. 7	1/0	—	—
MASS IN G, No. 12 (Latin)	1/0	1/6	2 6
Ditto (Latin and English) (Sol-fa, 0/9)	1/0	1/6	2/6
Ditto (Choruses only)	0/8	—	—
MASS IN D MINOR, No. 15	1/0	1/6	2/6
Ditto (Latin and English) (Sol-fa, 1/0)...	1/0	1/6	2/6
O GOD, WHEN THOU. (Sol-fa, 0/2)... First Motet	0/3	—	—
SPLENDENTE TE, DEUS ... First Motet	0/3	—	—

E. MUNDELLA.

VICTORY OF SONG (Female voices)	1/0	—	—

JOHN NAYLOR.

JEREMIAH	3/0	—	—

JOSEF NEŠVERA.

DE PROFUNDIS	2/6	—	—

E. A. NUNN.

MASS, IN C	2/0	—	—

E. CUTHBERT NUNN.

THE FAIRY SLIPPER (Children's Opera) (Sol-fa,0/8)	2/0	—	—

A. O'LEARY.

MASS OF ST. JOHN	1/3	—	—

REV. SIR FREDK. OUSELEY.

THE MARTYRDOM OF ST. POLYCARP	2/6	—	—

R. P. PAINE.

THE LORD REIGNETH (93rd Psalm)	1/0	—	—

PALESTRINA.

COMMUNION SERVICE (Missa Papæ Marcelli)	2/6	—	—
COMMUNION SERVICE (Assumpta est Maria)	2/6	—	—
MISSA ASSUMPTA EST MARIA	2/6	—	—
MISSA BREVIS	2/6	—	—
MISSA "O ADMIRABILE COMMERCIUM"	2/6	—	—
MISSA PAPÆ MARCELLI	2/0	—	—
STABAT MATER	1/6	—	—

H. W. PARKER.

A WANDERER'S PSALM	2/6	—	—
HORA NOVISSIMA	3/6	4/0	—
LEGEND OF ST. CHRISTOPHER	5/0	—	—
THE KOBOLDS	1/0	—	—

C. H. H. PARRY.

	Paper Cover.	Paper Boards.	Cloth Gilt.
AGAMEMNON (Greek Play)	3/0	—	—
A SONG OF DARKNESS AND LIGHT (Sol-fa,0/9)	2/0	—	—
BEYOND THESE VOICES THERE IS PEACE	2/6	—	—
BIRDS OF ARISTOPHANES (Greek Play)...	5/0	—	—
BLEST PAIR OF SIRENS (Sol-fa, 0/8)	1/0	—	—
(Ditto, English and German Words, 2 mark 50)			
DE PROFUNDIS (130th Psalm)	2/0	—	—
ETON	2/0	—	—
ETON MEMORIAL ODE	1/6	—	—
GLORIES OF OUR BLOOD AND STATE	1/0	—	—
INVOCATION TO MUSIC	2/6	—	—
JOB (Choruses only, Sol-fa, 1/0)	2/6	—	—
JUDITH (Choruses only, Sol-fa, 2/0)	5/0	6/0	7/6
KING SAUL (Choruses only, Sol-fa, 1/6).	5/0	6/0	7/6
L'ALLEGRO (Sol-fa, 1/6)	2/6	—	—
LOTOS-EATERS (The Choric Song)	2/0	—	—
LOVE THAT CASTETH OUT FEAR	2/6	—	—
MAGNIFICAT (Latin)	1/6	—	—
ODE ON ST. CECILIA'S DAY (Sol-fa, 1/0)	2/0	—	—
ODE TO MUSIC (Sol-fa, 0/6)	1/6	—	—
PIED PIPER OF HAMELIN (Sol-fa, 1/0)	2/0	2/6	—
PROMETHEUS UNBOUND	3/0	—	—
SOUL'S RANSOM (A Psalm of the Poor)	2/0	—	—
TE DEUM LAUDAMUS (Latin)	2/6	—	—
VISION OF LIFE (Sol-fa, 1/0)	2/6	—	—
VOCES CLAMANTIUM (The voices of them that cry)	2/0	—	—
WAR AND PEACE (Ode)...	3/0	—	—
Ditto Choruses and Words of Solos only, Tonic Sol-fa	1/6	—	—

B. PARSONS.

THE CRUSADER	3/6	—	—

T. M. PATTISON.

ANCIENT MARINER (Choruses, 1/0)	2/6	—	—
LAY OF THE LAST MINSTREL (Choruses, 1/0)...	2/6	—	—
LONDON CRIES	2/0	—	—
MAY DAY	1/0	—	—
MIRACLES OF CHRIST (Sol-fa, 0/6)	1 0	—	—

A. L. PEACE.

ST. JOHN THE BAPTIST (Sol-fa, 1/0)	2/6	—	—

PERGOLESI.

STABAT MATER (Female voices) (Sol-fa, 0/6)	1/0	—	—

CIRO PINSUTI.

PHANTOMS—FANTASMI NELL' OMBRA	1/0	—	—

PERCY PITT.

HOHENLINDEN (Men's voices)	1/6	—	—

JOHN POINTER.

THE SONG OF HAROLD HARFAGER (Male Voices) (Sol-fa, 0/6)	1/0	—	—

V. W. POPHAM.

EARLY SPRING	1/0	—	—

J. B. POWELL.

PANGE LINGUA (Sing, my tongue)	1/6	—	—

A. H. D. PRENDERGAST.

THE SECOND ADVENT...	1/6	—	—

F. W. PRIEST.

THE CENTURION'S SERVANT	0/8	—	—

C. E. PRITCHARD.

KUNACEPA	4/0	—	—

E. PROUT.

DAMON AND PHINTIAS (Male voices)	2/6	—	—
FREEDOM	1/0	—	—
HEREWARD	4/0	—	—
HUNDREDTH PSALM (Sol-fa, 0/4)	1/0	—	—
QUEEN AIMÉE (Female voices)	1/6	—	—
RED CROSS KNIGHT (Sol-fa, 2/0)	4/0	4/3	6/0

PURCELL.

DIDO AND ÆNEAS	2/6	—	—
KING ARTHUR	2/0	—	—
ODE ON ST. CECILIA'S DAY (Choruses only and words of Solos (Sol-fa, 0/8)	2/0	—	—
TE DEUM AND JUBILATE, IN D	1/0	—	—
Ditto (Edited by Dr. Bridge) (Sol-fa, 0/6)	1/0	—	—
Ditto (Latin arrangement by R. R. Terry)	1/0	—	—
THE MASQUE IN "DIOCLESIAN"	2/0	—	—

LADY RAMSAY.

THE BLESSED DAMOZEL	2/6	—	—

G. RATHBONE.

ORPHEUS (Power of Music) (Female voices)	1/6	—	—
(Ditto, Sol-fa, 0/6)			
VOGELWEID THE MINNESINGER (Operetta)	1/0	—	—
(Ditto, Sol-fa, 0/6)			

F. J. READ.

THE SONG OF HANNAH	1/0	—	—

J. F. H. READ.

	Paper Cover	Paper Boards	Cloth Gilt
BARTIMEUS ...	1/6	—	—
CARACTACUS ...	2/6	—	—
CONSECRATION OF THE BANNER	1/6	—	—
DEATH OF YOUNG ROMILLY	1/6	—	—
HAROLD ...	4/0	—	6,0
HESPERUS (Sol-fa, 0/9) ...	1/6	—	—
IN THE FOREST (Male voices)	1/0	—	—
PSYCHE (Choruses only, 2/0) ...	5/0	—	7/0

DOUGLAS REDMAN.

COR UNUM VIA UNA (Female voices)	1/6	—	—

C. T. REYNOLDS.

CHILDHOOD OF SAMUEL (Sol-fa, 1/0)	2/0	—	—

ARTHUR RICHARDS.

PUNCH AND JUDY (Operetta) (Sol-fa, 0/6)...	1/6	—	—
WAXWORK CARNIVAL (Operetta) Sol-fa, 0/8)	2/0	—	—

J. V. ROBERTS

JONAH ...	2/0	—	—
THE PASSION ...	1/6	2/0	—

R. WALKER ROBSON.

CHRISTUS TRIUMPHATOR ...	3/6	—	—

W. S. ROCKSTRO.

THE GOOD SHEPHERD	2/6	—	—

J. L. ROECKEL.

LITTLE SNOW-WHITE (Operetta) (Sol-fa, 0/9)	2/0	—	—
THE HOURS (Operetta) (Sol-fa, 0/9) ...	2/0	—	—
THE SILVER PENNY (Operetta) (Sol-fa, 0/9)	2/0	—	—

EDMUND ROGERS.

THE FOREST FLOWER (Female voices) ...	1/6	—	—

ROLAND ROGERS.

FLORABEL (Female voices) (Sol-fa, 1/0)	1/6	—	—
PRAYER AND PRAISE (Oblong)	4/0	—	—

F. ROLLASON.

STOOD THE MOURNFUL MOTHER WEEPING	1/6	—	—

ROMBERG.

HARMONY OF THE SPHERES ...	1/0	—	—
LAY OF THE BELL (Sol-fa, 0/8) ...	1/0	1/6	2/6
TE DEUM ...	1/0	—	—
TRANSIENT AND THE ETERNAL	1/0	—	—
(Ditto, Sol-fa, 0/4)			

C. B. ROOTHAM.

ANDROMEDA ...	2/6	—	—

ROSSINI.

MOSES IN EGYPT ...	6/0	6/6	7/6
STABAT MATER (Sol-fa, 1/0) ...	1/0	1/6	2/6
Ditto (Choruses only)...	0/6	1/0	—

CHARLES B. RUTENBER.

DIVINE LOVE ...	2/6	—	—

JOSEPH RYELANDT.

DE KOMST DES HEEREN (The coming of the Lord)	8/0	—	—

ED. SACHS.

KING-CUPS ...	1/0	—	—
WATER LILIES ...	1/0	—	—

C. SAINTON-DOLBY.

FLORIMEL (Female voices) ...	2/6	—	—

CAMILLE SAINT-SAËNS.

THE HEAVENS DECLARE—CŒLI ENARRANT (19th Psalm),...	1/6	—	—

W. H. SANGSTER.

ELYSIUM ...	1/0	—	—

FRANK J. SAWYER.

THE SOUL'S FORGIVENESS ...	1/0	—	—
THE STAR IN THE EAST ...	2/6	—	—

C. SCHAFER.

OUR BEAUTIFUL WORLD (Operetta)	2/6	—	—

H. W. SCHARTAU.

CHRISTMAS HOLIDAYS (Female voices)	0/6	—	—

SCHUBERT.

COMMUNION SERVICE, IN A FLAT ...	2/0	—	3/6
Ditto, IN B FLAT ...	2/0	—	3/6
Ditto, IN C ...	2/0	—	3/6
Ditto, IN E FLAT ...	2/0	2/6	4/0
Ditto, IN F ...	2/0	—	3/6
Ditto, IN G ...	2/0	—	3/6
LARARUS (Easter) ...	1/6	—	—
MASS, IN A FLAT ...	1/0	1/6	2/6
Do., IN B FLAT ...	1/0	1/6	2/6
Do., IN C ...	1/0	1/6	2/6
Do., IN E FLAT ...	2/0	2/6	4/0
Do., IN F (Sol-fa, 0/9) ...	1/0	1/6	2/6
Do., IN G ...	1/0	1/6	2/6
SONG OF MIRIAM (Sol-fa, 0/6)	1/0	—	—
(Ditto, Welsh Words, Sol-fa, 0/6)			
SONG OF THE SPIRITS OVER THE WATERS (Male voices) (Sol-fa, 0/6) ...	1/0	—	—

SCHUMANN.

	Paper Cover	Paper Boards	Cloth Gilt
ADVENT HYMN, "In Lowly Guise"	1/0	—	—
FAUST ...	3/0	3/6	5/0
KING'S SON ...	1/0	—	—
LUCK OF EDENHALL (Male voices)	1/6	—	—
MANFRED ...	1/0	—	—
MIGNON'S REQUIEM ...	1/0	—	—
MINSTREL'S CURSE ...	1/6	—	—
NEW YEAR'S SONG (Sol-fa, 0/6)	1/0	—	—
PARADISE AND THE PERI (Sol-fa, 1/6) ...	2/6	3/0	4/0
PILGRIMAGE OF THE ROSE...	1/0	1/6	2/0
REQUIEM ...	2/0	—	—
SONG OF THE NIGHT ...	0/9	—	—

H. SCHÜTZ.

THE PASSION OF OUR LORD ...	1/0	—	—

BERTRAM LUARD-SELBY.

DYING SWAN ...	1/0	—	—
FAKENHAM GHOST ...	1/6	—	—
"HELENA IN TROAS" ...	3/6	—	—
SUMMER BY THE SEA (Female) (Sol-fa 0/6)	1/6	—	—
WAITS OF BREMEN (Children) (Sol-fa, 0/6)	1/6	—	—

H. R. SHELLEY.

VEXILLA REGIS (The Royal Banners forward go)	2/6	—	—

E. SILAS.

COMMUNION SERVICE, IN C ...	1/6	—	—
JOASH ...	4/0	—	—
MASS, IN C ...	1/0	—	—

R. SLOMAN.

CONSTANTIA ...	2/6	—	—
SUPPLICATION AND PRAISE ...	2/6	—	—

HENRY SMART.

KING RENÉ'S DAUGHTER (Female voices)	2/6	—	—
(Ditto, Sol-fa, 1/0)			
SING TO THE LORD ...	1/0	—	—
THE BRIDE OF DUNKERRON (Sol-fa, 1/0)	2/0	2/6	4/0

J. M. SMIETON.

ARIADNE (Sol-fa, 0/9) ...	2/0	—	—
CONNLA ...	2/6	—	—
KING ARTHUR (Sol-fa, 1/0) ...	2/6	—	—

ALICE MARY SMITH.

ODE TO THE NORTH-EAST WIND ...	1/0	—	—
ODE TO THE PASSIONS ...	2/0	—	—
THE RED KING (Men's voices)...	1/0	—	—
THE SONG OF THE LITTLE BALTUNG (ditto)	1/0	—	—
(Ditto, Sol-fa, 0/8)			

E. M. SMYTH.

MASS, IN D ...	2/6	—	—

A. SOMERVELL.

CHARGE OF THE LIGHT BRIGADE (Sol-fa, 0/4)	0/9	—	—
ELEGY ...	1/6	—	—
ENCHANTED PALACE (Operetta) (Sol-fa, 0/8)	2/0	—	—
FORSAKEN MERMAN (Sol-fa, 0/8) ...	1/6	—	—
KING THRUSHBEARD (Operetta) (Sol-fa, 0/9)	2/0	—	—
KNAVE OF HEARTS (Operetta) (Sol-fa, 0/8)	2/0	—	—
MASS, IN C MINOR ...	2/6	—	—
ODE ON THE INTIMATIONS OF IMMORTALITY	2/0	—	—
ODE TO THE SEA (Sol-fa, 1/0) ...	2/0	—	—
POWER OF SOUND (Sol-fa, 1/0) ...	2/0	—	—
PRINCESS ZARA (Operetta) (Sol-fa, 0/9)	2/0	—	—
SEVEN LAST WORDS ...	1/0	—	—

R. SOMERVILLE.

THE 'PRENTICE PILLAR (Opera) ...	2/0	—	—

W. H. SPEER.

THE JACKDAW OF RHEIMS ...	2/0	—	—

SPOHR.

CALVARY ...	2/6	3/0	4/0
CHRISTIAN'S PRAYER ...	1/0	1/6	2/6
FALL OF BABYLON ...	3/0	3/6	5/0
FROM THE DEEP I CALLED ...	0/6	—	—
GOD IS MY SHEPHERD ...	0/9	—	—
GOD, THOU ART GREAT (Sol-fa, 0/6) ...	1/0	—	—
HOW LOVELY ARE THY DWELLINGS FAIR...	0/8	—	—
HYMN TO ST. CECILIA...	1/0	—	—
JEHOVAH, LORD OF HOSTS ...	0/4	—	—
LAST JUDGMENT (Sol-fa, 1/0) ...	1/0	1/6	2/6
Ditto (Choruses only) ...	0/6	1/0	—
MASS (for 5 solo voices and double choir) ...	2/0	—	—

JOHN STAINER.

ST. MARY MAGDALEN (Sol-fa, 1/0) ...	2/0	2/6	4/0
THE CRUCIFIXION (Sol-fa, 0/9) ...	1/6	2/0	—
THE DAUGHTER OF JAIRUS (Sol-fa, 0/9) ...	1/6	2/0	—

C. VILLIERS STANFORD.

	Paper Cover.	Paper Boards.	Cloth Gilt.
BATTLE OF THE BALTIC	1/6	—	—
CARMEN SÆCULARE	1/6	—	—
COMMUNION SERVICE, IN G	2/6	—	—
EAST TO WEST	1/6	—	—
EDEN	5/0	6/0	7/6
EUMENIDES	3/0	—	—
GOD IS OUR HOPE (46th Psalm)	2/0	—	—
MASS, IN G MAJOR	2/6	—	—
ŒDIPUS REX (Male voices)	3/0	—	—
REVENGE (SOL-FA, 0/9)	1/6	—	—
(Ditto, German Words, 2 Mark.)			
VOYAGE OF MAELDUNE	2/6	3/0	4/0

F. R. STATHAM.

VASCO DA GAMA	2/6	—	—

BRUCE STEANE.

THE ASCENSION	2/6	3/0	4/0

D. STEPHEN.

THE LAIRD O'COCKPEN (SOL-FA, 0/6)	1/0	—	—

H. W. STEWARDSON.

GIDEON	4/0	—	—

STEFAN STOCKER.

SONG OF THE FATES	1/0	—	—

SIGISMOND STOJOWSKI.

SPRING-TIME	1/0	—	—

J. STORER.

MASS OF OUR LADY OF RANSOM	1/6	—	—
THE TOURNAMENT	1/6	—	—

E. C. SUCH.

GOD IS OUR REFUGE (46th Psalm)	1/0	—	—
NARCISSUS AND ECHO	3/0	—	—
Ditto (Choruses only)			

ARTHUR SULLIVAN.

GOLDEN LEGEND (SOL-FA, 2/0)	3/6	4/0	5/0
KING ARTHUR, INCIDENTAL MUSIC	1/6	—	—
ODE FOR THE COLONIAL AND INDIAN EXHIBITION	1/0	—	—
TE DEUM FESTIVAL (SOL-FA, 1/0)	1/0	1/6	2/6
TE DEUM (A Thanksgiving for Victory) (SOL-FA, 0/9)	1/0	—	—

T. W. SURETTE.

THE EVE OF ST. AGNES	2/0	—	—

W. TAYLOR.

ST. JOHN THE BAPTIST	—	4/0	—

A. GORING THOMAS.

THE SUN-WORSHIPPERS (SOL-FA, 0/9)	1/0	—	—

D. THOMAS.

LLYN Y FAN (THE VAN LAKE) (SOL-FA, 1/6)	3/6	—	—

E. H. THORNE.

BE MERCIFUL UNTO ME	1/0	—	—

G. W. TORRANCE.

THE REVELATION	5/0	—	—

BERTHOLD TOURS.

A FESTIVAL ODE	1/0	—	—
THE HOME OF TITANIA (Female voices)	1/6	—	—
(Ditto, SOL-FA, 0/6)			

FERRIS TOZER.

BALAAM AND BALAK	2/6	—	—
KING NEPTUNE'S DAUGHTER (Female voices)	1/6	—	—
(Ditto, SOL-FA, 0/6)			

P. TSCHAÏKOWSKY.

NATURE AND LOVE (Female voices) (SOL-FA, 0/4)	1/0	—	—

VAN BREE.

ST. CECILIA'S DAY (SOL-FA, 0/9)	1/0	1/6	2/6

CHARLES VINCENT.

THE LITTLE MERMAID (Female voices)	1/6	—	—
THE VILLAGE QUEEN (Female voices) (SOL-FA, 0/6)	1/6	—	—

A. L. VINGOE.

THE MAGICIAN (Operetta) (SOL-FA, 0/9)	2/0	—	—

W. S. VINNING.

SONG OF THE PASSION (according to St. John)	1/6	—	—

S. P. WADDINGTON.

	Paper Cover.	Paper Boards.	Cloth Gilt.
JOHN GILPIN (SOL-FA, 0/8)	2/0	—	—
WHIMLAND (Operetta) (SOL-FA, 0/8)	2/0	—	—

R. WAGNER.

HOLY SUPPER OF THE APOSTLES	2/0	—	—

W. M. WAIT.

GOD WITH US	2/0	—	—
GOOD SAMARITAN	2/0	—	—
ST. ANDREW	2/0	—	—

ERNEST WALKER.

A HYMN TO DIONYSUS	1/0	—	—
ODE TO A NIGHTINGALE	1/0	—	—

R. H. WALTHEW.

THE PIED PIPER OF HAMELIN	2/0	—	—

H. W. WAREING.

COURT OF QUEEN SUMMERGOLD (Operetta) (SOL-FA, 0/6)	1/0	—	—
HO-HO OF THE GOLDEN BELT (Humorous Cantata for Children) (SOL-FA, 0/6)	1/0	—	—
PRINCESS SNOWFLAKE (Operetta) (SOL-FA, 0/6)	1/0	—	—
WRECK OF THE HESPERUS	1/6	—	—

HENRY WATSON.

A PSALM OF THANKSGIVING	1/0	—	—
IN PRAISE OF THE DIVINE (Masonic Ode)	2/0	—	—

WEBER.

COMMUNION SERVICE, IN E FLAT	1/6	—	—
IN CONSTANT ORDER (Hymn)	1/6	—	—
JUBILEE CANTATA	1/0	1/6	—
MASS IN E FLAT (Latin and English)	1/0	1/6	2/6
Do., IN G (Latin and English)	1/0	1/6	2/6
PRECIOSA (Opera) (Choruses only, 0/6)	1/0	—	—
THREE SEASONS	1/0	—	—

THEOPHIL WENDT.

ODE	1/6	—	—

S. WESLEY.

DIXIT DOMINUS	1/0	—	—
EXULTATE DEO (Sing aloud with gladness)	0/6	—	—
IN EXITU ISRAEL (English or Latin Words)	0/4	—	—

S. S. WESLEY.

O LORD, THOU ART MY GOD	1/0	—	—

FLORENCE E. WEST.

A MIDSUMMER'S DAY (Operetta) (SOL-FA, 0/6)	1/6	—	—

JOHN E. WEST.

A SONG OF ZION	1/0	—	—
LORD, I HAVE LOVED THE HABITATION OF THY HOUSE	1/0	—	—
MAY-DAY REVELS (Female voices) (SOL-FA, 0/4)	1/6	—	—
SEED-TIME AND HARVEST (SOL-FA, 1/0)	2/0	—	—
THE STORY OF BETHLEHEM (SOL-FA, 0/9)	1/6	—	—

ARTHUR N. WIGHT.

THE MINSTREL'S CURSE	1/6	—	—

C. LEE WILLIAMS.

A FESTIVAL HYMN	0/8	—	—
A HARVEST SONG	1/6	—	—
GETHSEMANE	2/0	2/6	—
THE LAST NIGHT AT BETHANY (SOL-FA, 1/0)	2/0	2/6	—

A. E. WILSHIRE.

GOD IS OUR HOPE (Psalm 46)	2/0	—	—

THOMAS WINGHAM.

MASS, IN D (Regina Cœli)	3/0	—	—
TE DEUM (Latin)	1/6	—	—

CHAS. WOOD.

ODE TO THE WEST WIND	1/0	—	—

F. C. WOODS.

A GREYPORT LEGEND (1797) (Male voices)	1/0	—	—
(Ditto, SOL-FA, 0/6)			
KING HAROLD (SOL-FA, 0/9)	1/6	—	—
OLD MAY-DAY (Female voices) (SOL-FA, 0/6)	1/6	—	—

E. M. WOOLLEY.

THE CAPTIVE SOUL (Soprano, Mezzo, Contralto, and Tenor Soli, and Chorus for Female Voices)	1/6	—	—

D. YOUNG.

THE BLESSED DAMOZEL	1/6	—	—

LONDON : NOVELLO AND COMPANY, LIMITED.